cooee mittigar

A STORY ON DARUG SONGLINES

JASMINE SEYMOUR & LEANNE MULGO WATSON

Magabala
BOOKS

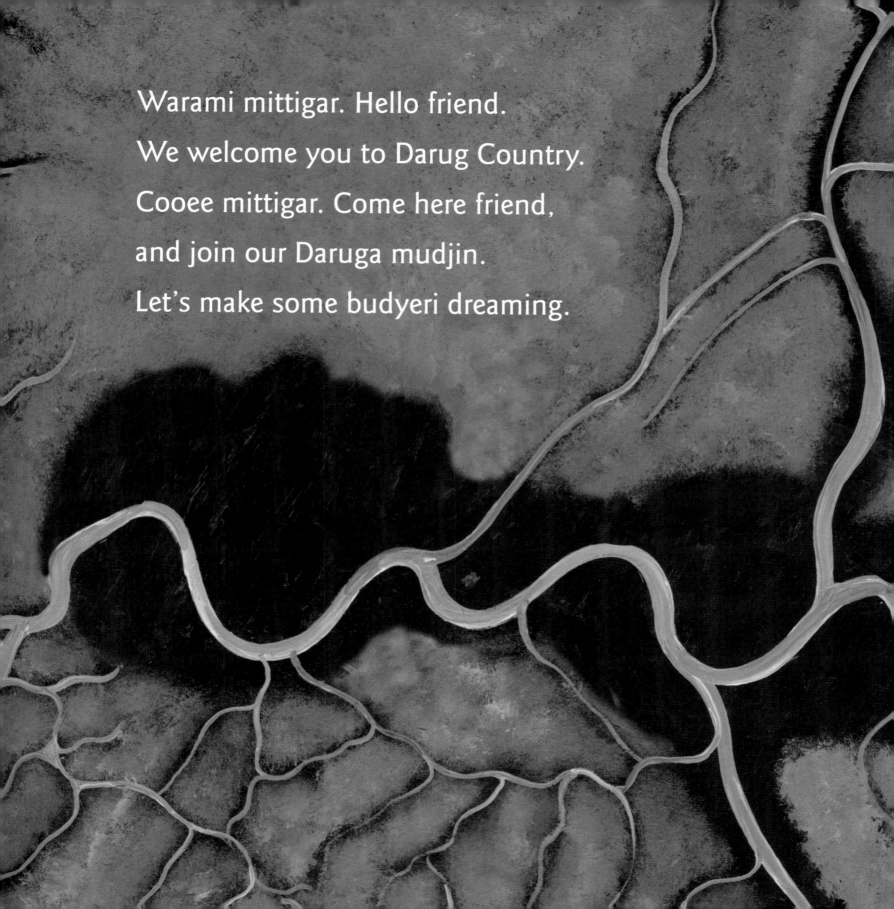

Warami mittigar. Hello friend.

We welcome you to Darug Country.

Cooee mittigar. Come here friend,

and join our Daruga mudjin.

Let's make some budyeri dreaming.

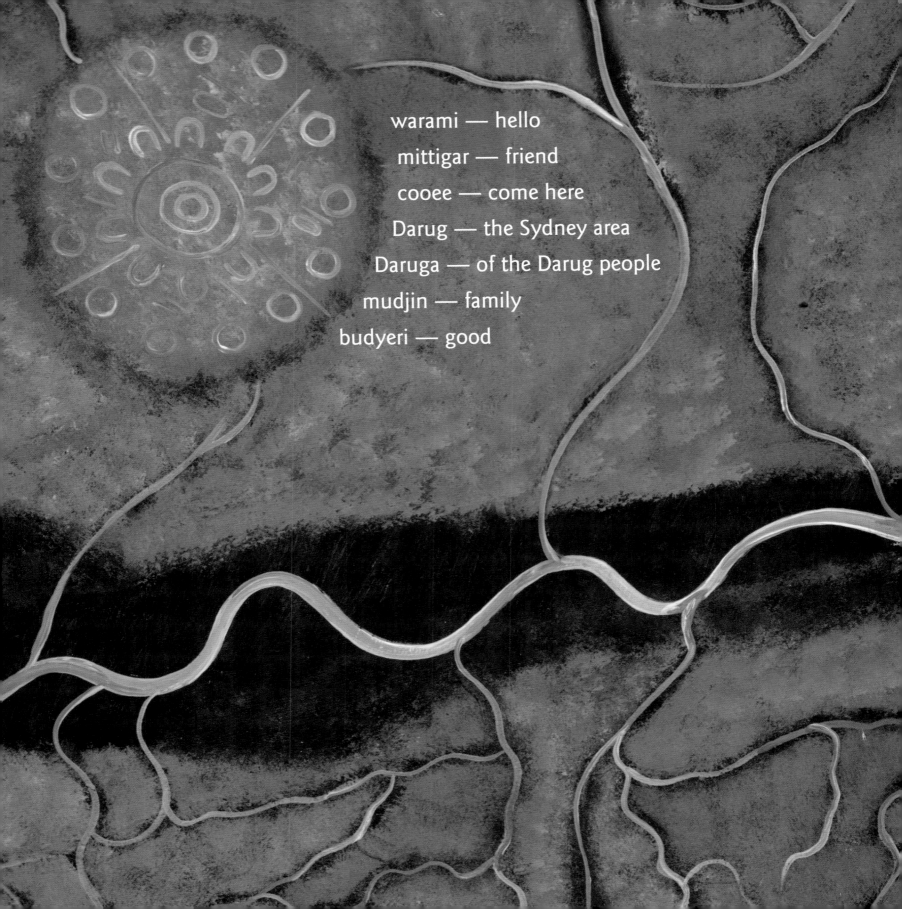

warami — hello

mittigar — friend

cooee — come here

Darug — the Sydney area

Daruga — of the Darug people

mudjin — family

budyeri — good

Ngaya Mulgo

Boorooberongal Daruga dalang.

I am Black Swan from the

Grey Kangaroo people of the Sydney area.

Yana with me and listen to the yabun

that beats with my bootboot.

I will teach you about Darug Life.

ngaya — I am

Mulgo — Black Swan

Boorooberongal — Grey Kangaroo people

Darug — the Sydney area

Daruga — of the Darug people

dalang — words off my tongue

yana — walk

yabun — instrumental music made by clapping sticks

bootboot — heart

Follow me on Nura as we move through
the minak and darrabura.

Yana with me in Biaimi's footsteps through
the times of yanada, yiluk and birrong.

In the long, long ago, in the now and forever,
Darug dreaming was, has, and will be sung
into the songlines of Nura by its creation peoples,
yellamundie, yibban-da, animals and lands.

Nura — Country   minak — night   darrabura — day
yana — walk   Biaimi — dreaming ancestor spirit
yanada — moon   yiluk — sun   Darug — the Sydney area
birrong — stars   yellamundie — storyteller   yibban-da — singing

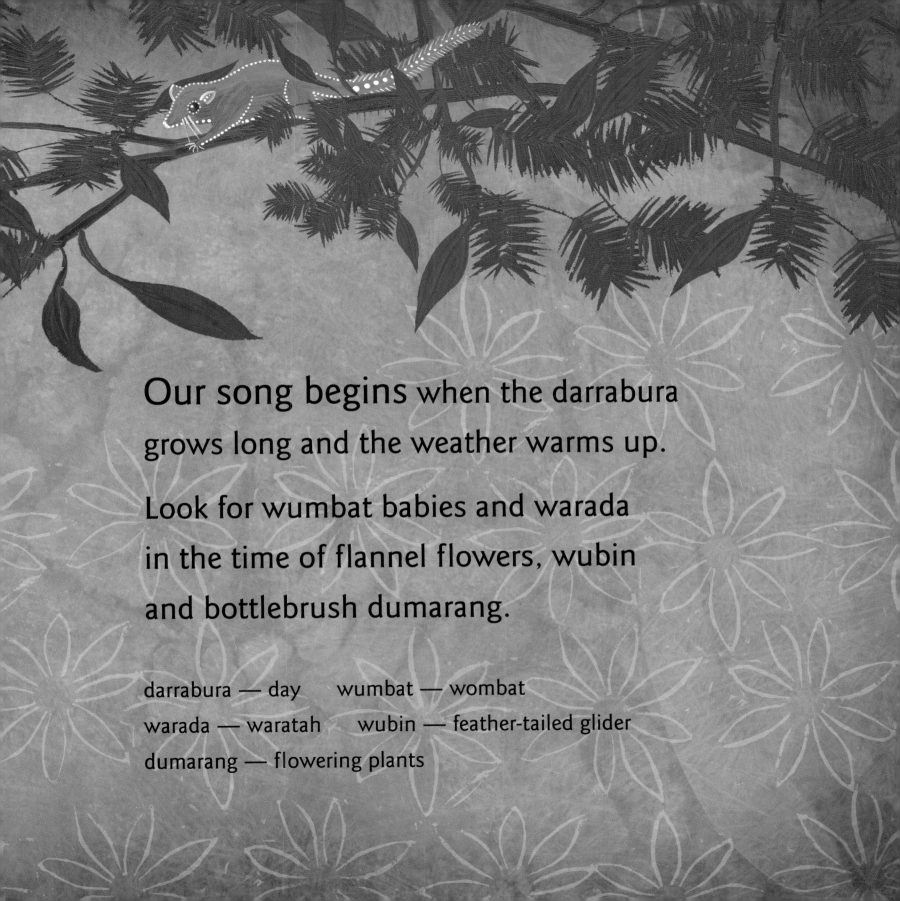

Our song begins when the darrabura
grows long and the weather warms up.

Look for wumbat babies and warada
in the time of flannel flowers, wubin
and bottlebrush dumarang.

darrabura — day   wumbat — wombat
warada — waratah   wubin — feather-tailed glider
dumarang — flowering plants

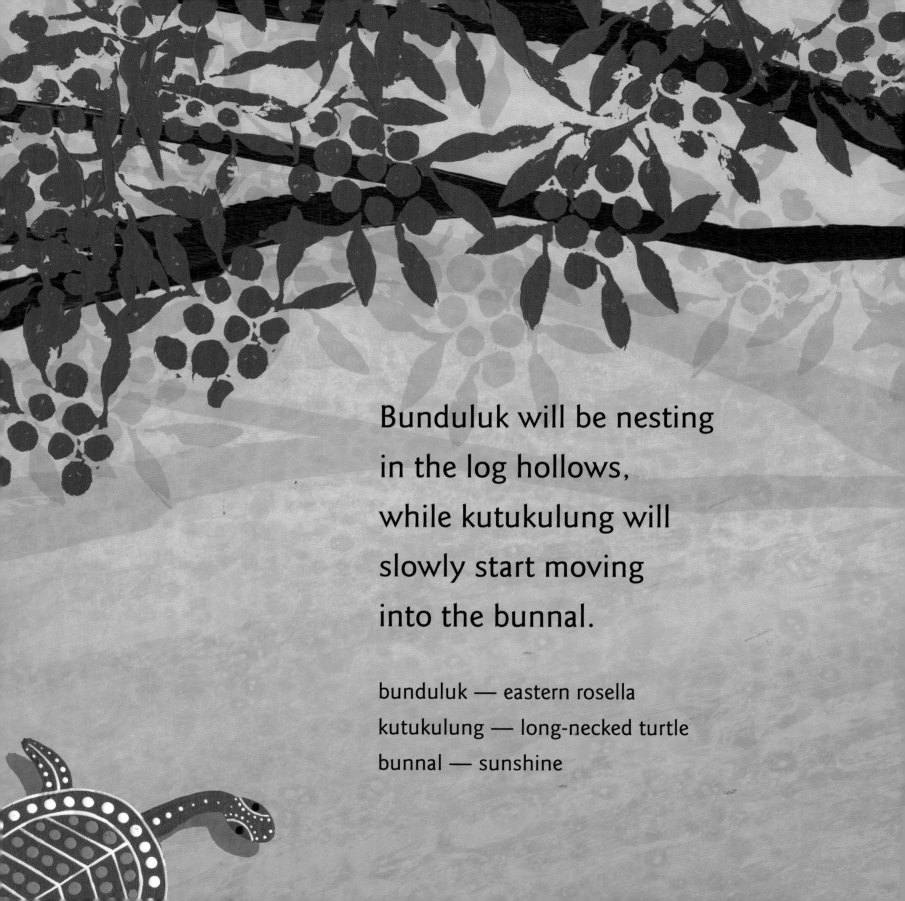

Bunduluk will be nesting
in the log hollows,
while kutukulung will
slowly start moving
into the bunnal.

bunduluk — eastern rosella
kutukulung — long-necked turtle
bunnal — sunshine

Next comes the time of yuruka,
walan and manga manga.
Storm time has arrived.

yuruka — hot
walan — rain
manga manga — lightning

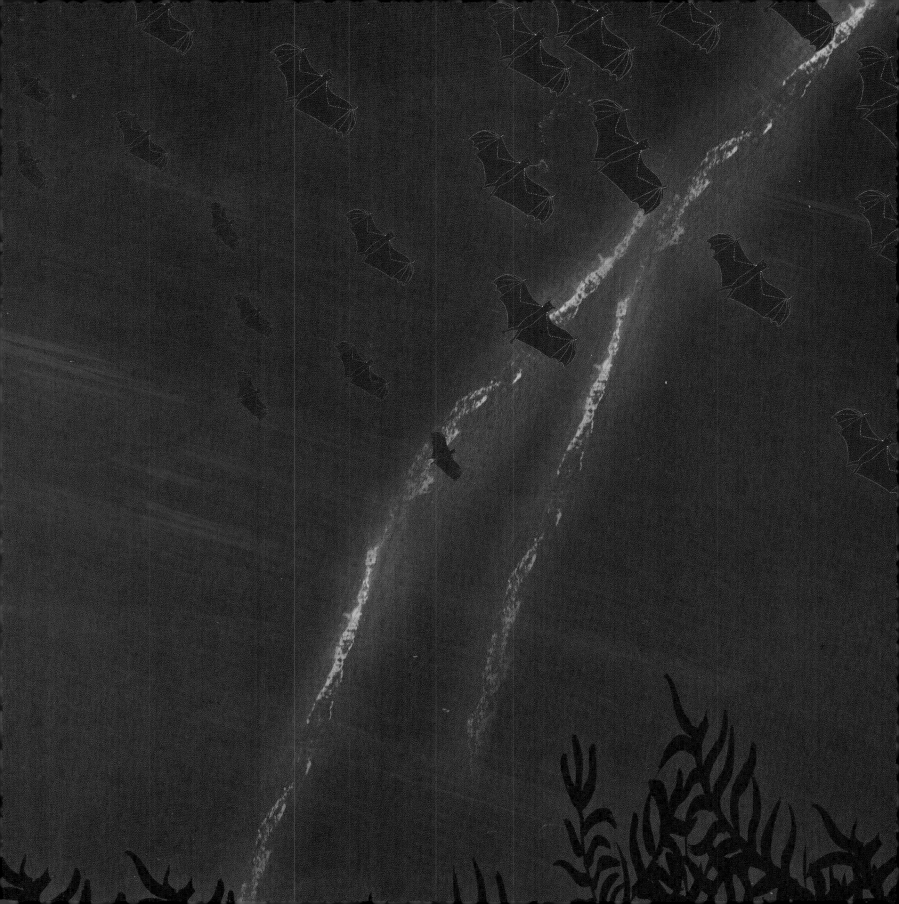

As the weather warms more
watch out for reptiles!
Look out for jirrabity and wirriga
as they move into the bunnal.

jirrabity — black snake
wirriga — goanna
bunnal — sunshine

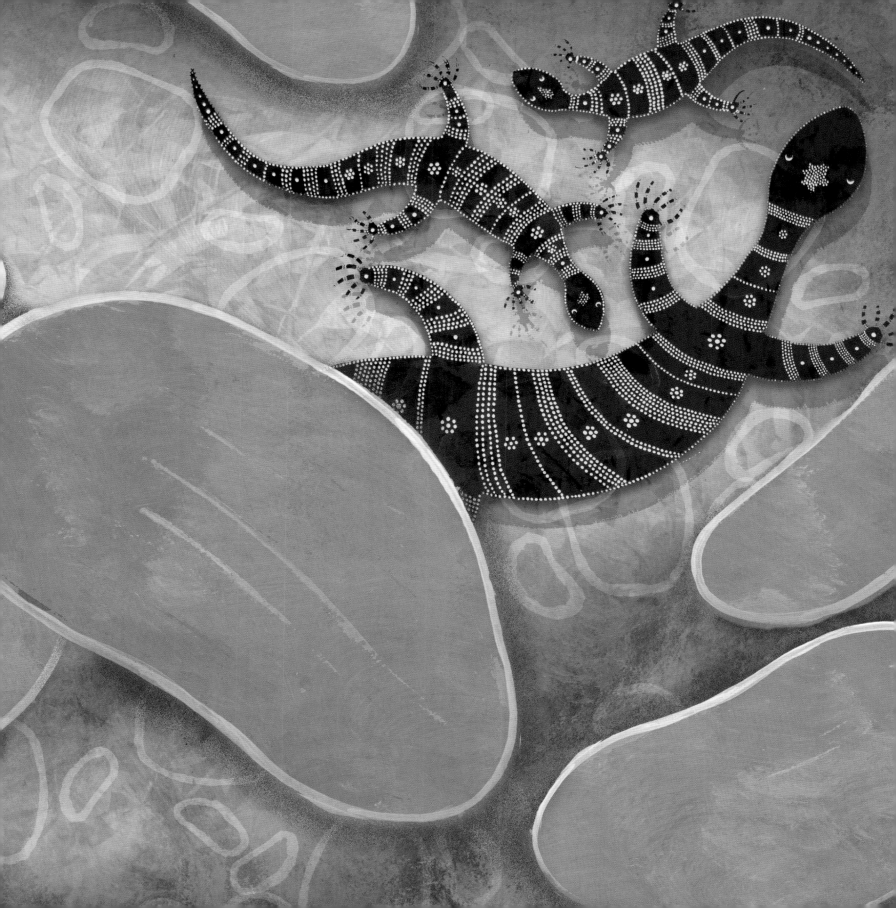

In the time of yuruka and burara
Elders tell us not to hunt the buru.

yuruka — hot
burara — dry
buru — kangaroo

After the yuruka, gurbuny time arrives.
Listen for the garad cry and watch for
the golden orb marraygong.

yuruka — hot   gurbuny — fog
garad — black cockatoo   marraygong — spider

In the time of the Mariong,
gaze at the birrong
and see her resting above us
in the minak bura.
When she has aligned herself
with Nura, it is time for
Mariong dreaming.

Mariong — emu (constellation)
birrong — stars   minak — night
bura — sky   Nura — Country

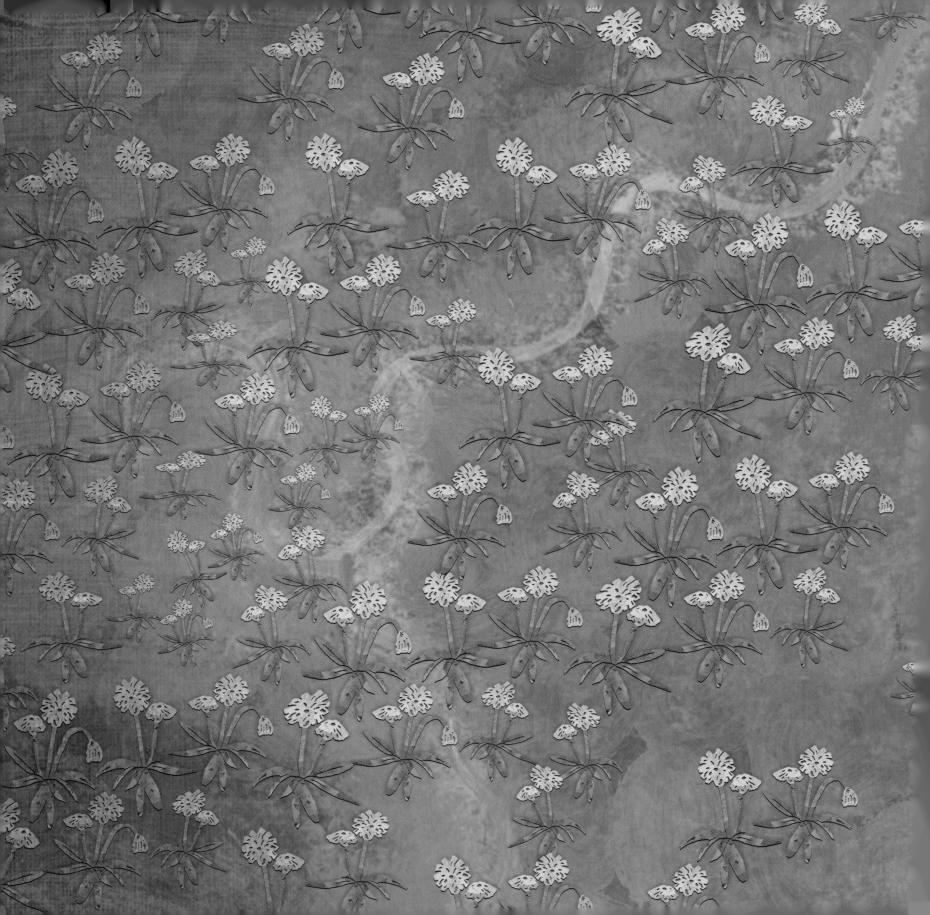

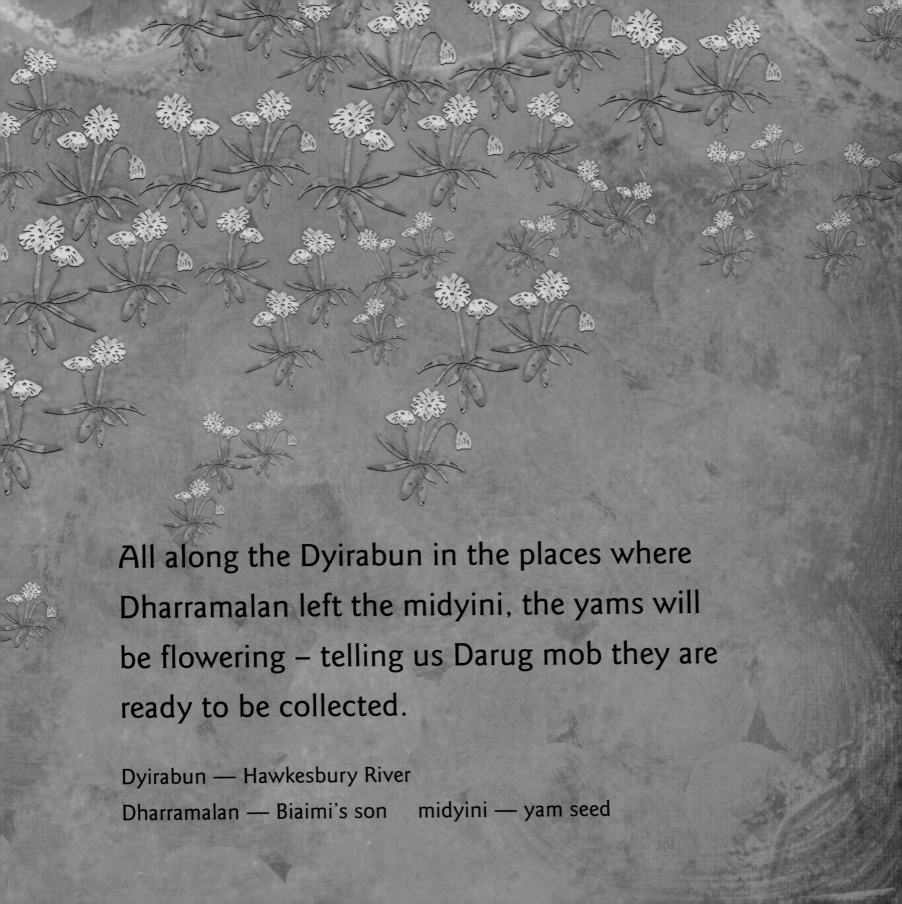

All along the Dyirabun in the places where
Dharramalan left the midyini, the yams will
be flowering – telling us Darug mob they are
ready to be collected.

Dyirabun — Hawkesbury River

Dharramalan — Biaimi's son   midyini — yam seed

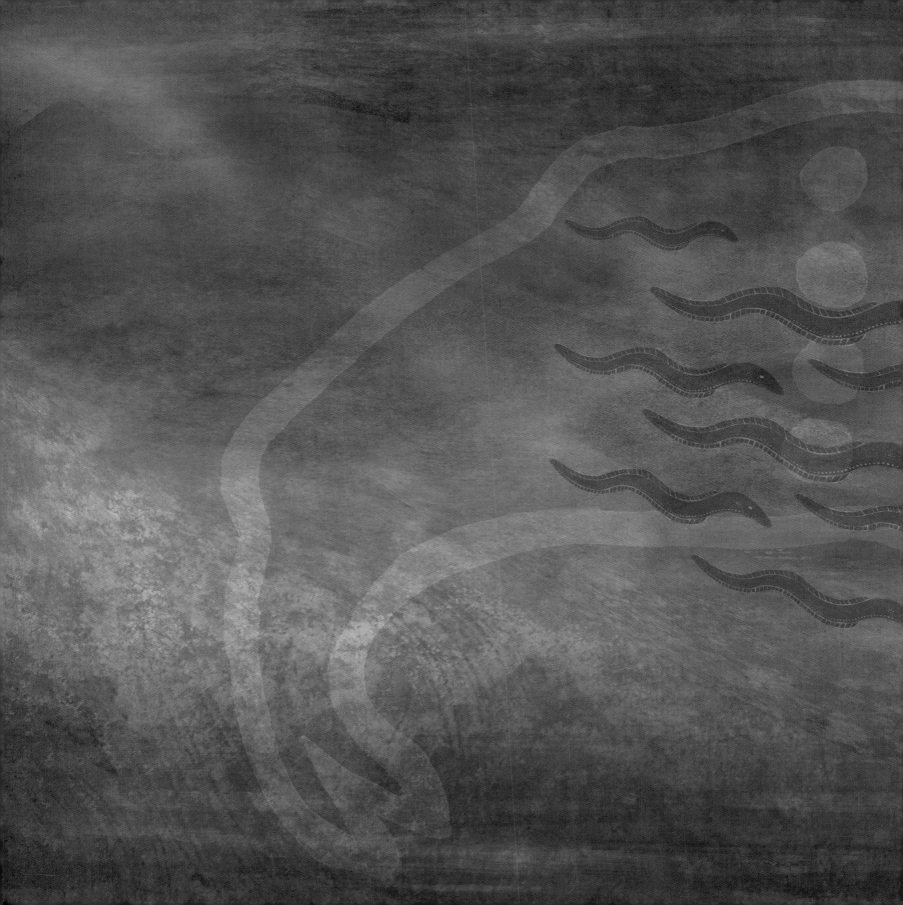

When the wandanguli blooms,
watch bara swim downstream
and out to sea.

wandanguli — wattle

bara — eel

Light barabung on the ground
and gwarra from the buruwi brings
the time for fire stick farming.
Guwiyang renews the undergrowth
and helps spread seed.

barabung — dew
gwarra — wind
buruwi — east
guwiyang — fire

Dingu babies start to arrive.
Warami wiyanga, biyanga,
djuramin and babana.

dingu — dingo
warami — hello
wiyanga — mother
biyanga — father
djuramin — sister
babana — brother

Soon dagara will come.
Watch for barugin wianga on the move.
Look for barugin mulabu marching
behind her – helping her to nest
in the sand.

dagara — frost   barugin — echidna
wiyanga — mother   mulabu — men

During dagara, gulgadya will bloom –
ready to be turned into spears.

dagara — frost
gulgadya — grasstree

When bayinmarri starts to blow,
Nura gets ready for dumarang
and gaban collecting.

bayinmarri — westerly wind
Nura — Country
dumarang — flowering plants
gaban — egg

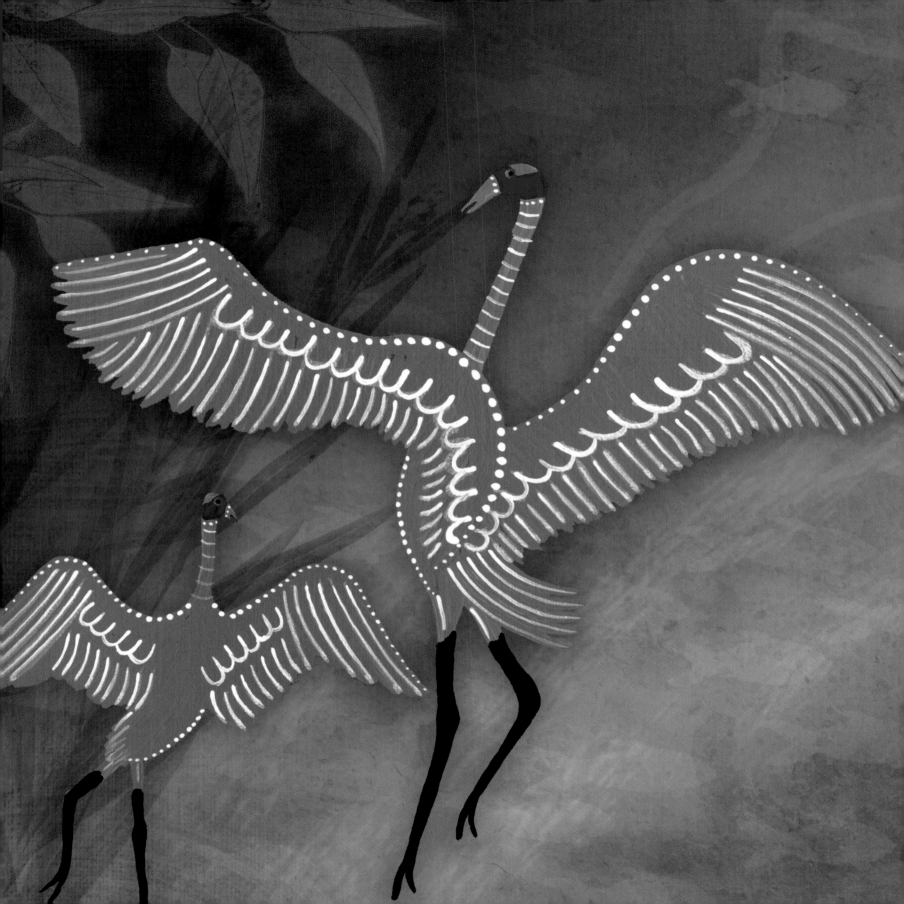

When durali dance
it is time to hold a ceremony.
We gather our mob
and celebrate the time of plenty.

durali — brolga

Now it is my time and
the songlines will begin again.

I, Mulgo, will rest
and make my nest ready,
for my new mudjin.

Mulgo — Black Swan
mudjin — family

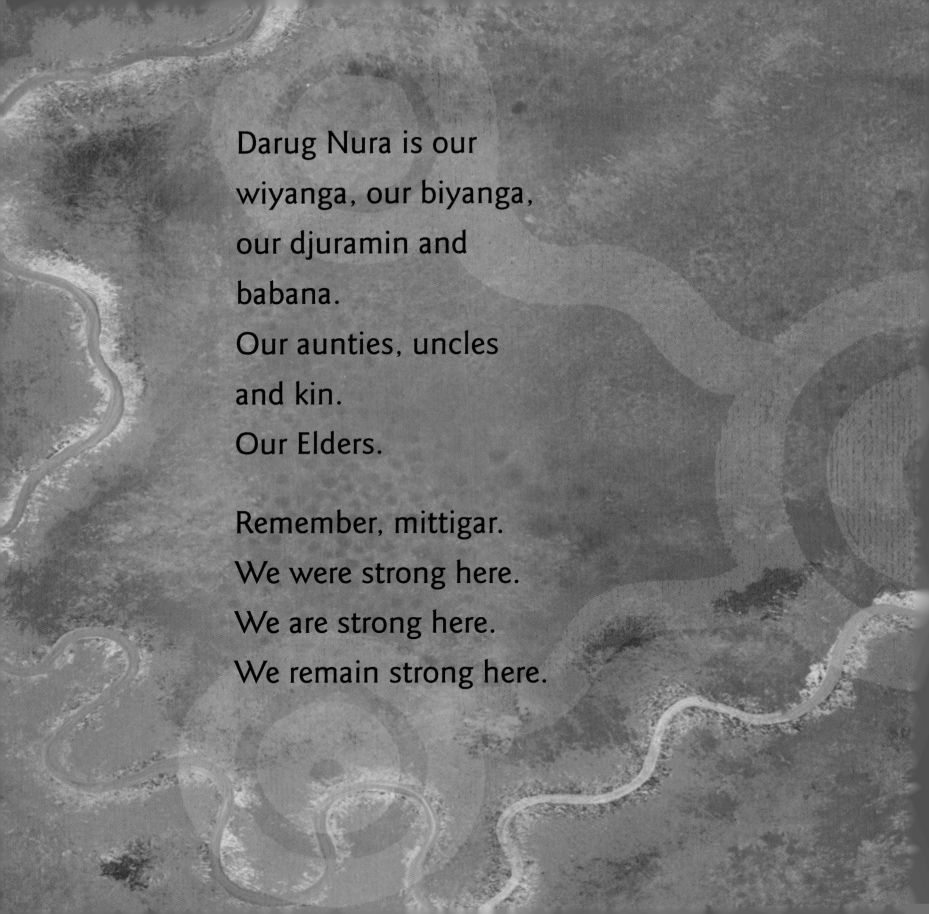

Darug Nura is our
wiyanga, our biyanga,
our djuramin and
babana.
Our aunties, uncles
and kin.
Our Elders.

Remember, mittigar.
We were strong here.
We are strong here.
We remain strong here.

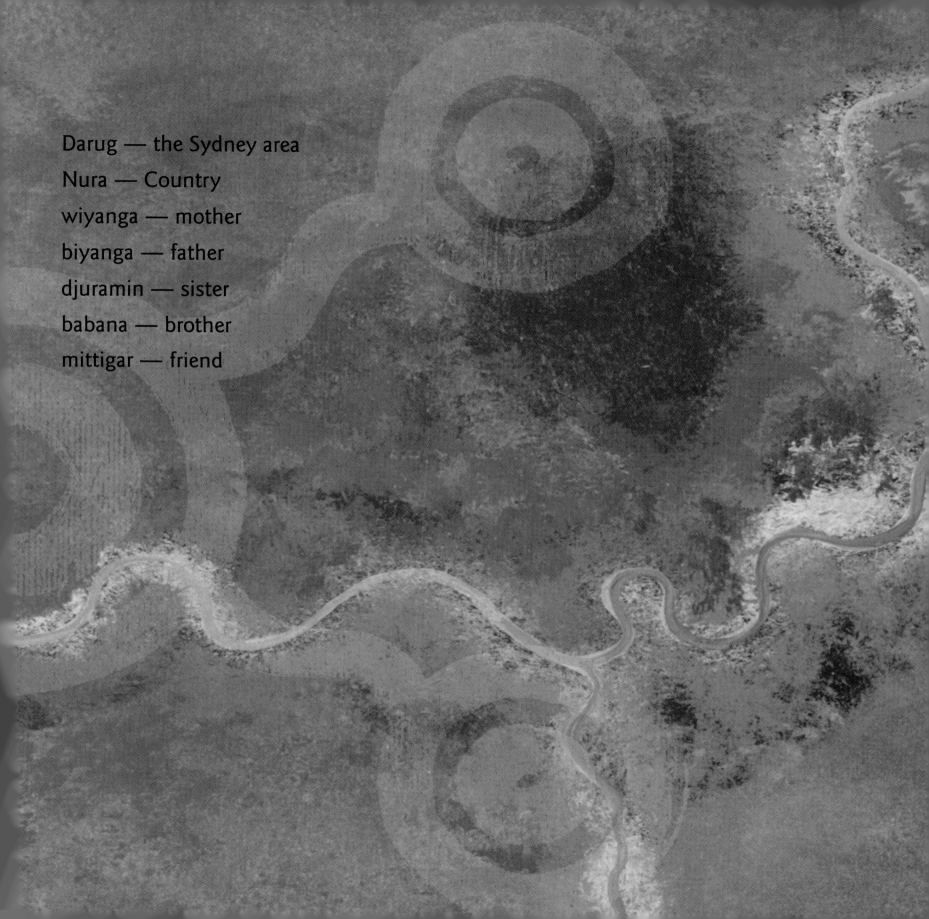

Darug — the Sydney area

Nura — Country

wiyanga — mother

biyanga — father

djuramin — sister

babana — brother

mittigar — friend

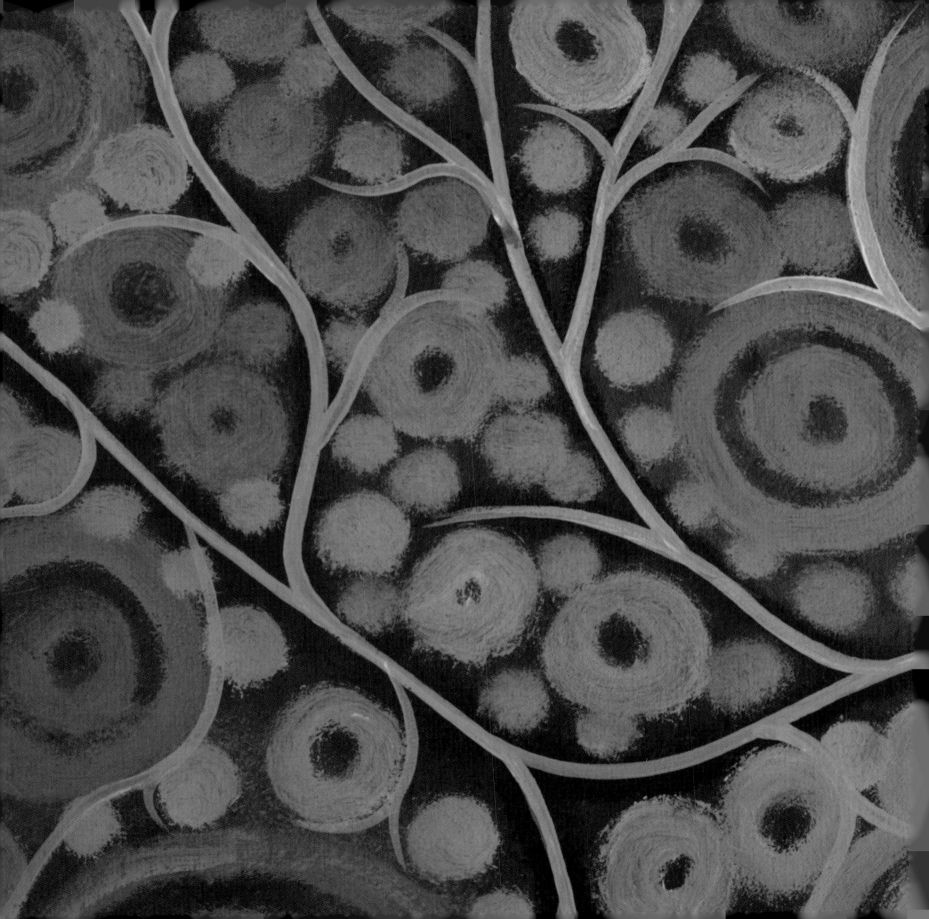

Cooee mittigar.
Tread softly on our lands.
Know that this dreaming
was here.
Is still here.
Will be forever.
Yanu. Yanu mittigar.

cooee — come here
mittigar — friend
yanu — goodbye

Darug language used in this book

babana — *ba ban na*
brother

bara — *ba ra*
eel

barabung — *bay ra boong*
dew

barugin — *bur roo gin*
echidna

barura — *baru ra*
dry

bayinmarri — *bayin marri*
westerly wind

Biaimi — *bi am ee*
dreaming ancestor spirit

birrong — *bir ong*
stars

biyanga — *bee yan ga*
father

Boorooberongal — *boo roo ber on gal*
Grey Kangaroo People

bootboot — *bud bud*
heart

budyeri — *bood jer ee*
good

bunduluk — *bundle uk*
eastern rosella

bunnal — *bun al*
sunshine

bura — *boor ra*
sky

buru — *boo roo*
kangaroo

buruwi — *boo roo wee*
east

cooee — *koo ee*
come here

dagara — *daga ra*
frost

dalang — *da lang*
words off my tongue

darrabura — *darra bura*
day

Darug — *da rug*
Country and people of the Sydney basin

Daruga — *da ru ga*
of the Darug people

Dharramalan — *dara moolan*
Biaimi's son

dingu — *din goo*
dingo

djuramin — *jura min*
sister

dumarang — *dooma rang*
flowering plant

durali — *du ra li*
brolga

Dyirabun — *gee ra bun*
Hawkesbury River

gaban — *gab an*
egg

garad — *kar ratt*
black cockatoo

gulgadya — *gul gad ya*
grasstree

gurbuny — *kur pu nya*
fog

guwiyang — *goo ee ang*
fire

gwarra — *g worra*
wind

jirrabity — *jirrab ity*
black snake

kutukulung — *kutu ku lung*
long-necked turtle

manga manga —
man ga man ga
lightning

mariong — *mari ong*
emu

marraygong —
marra ya gong
spider

midyini — *mid yini*
yam seed

minak — *min ak*
night

mittigar — *mitt ee gar*
friend

mudjin — *mood jin*
family

mulabu — *moola boo*
men

Mulgo — *mul go*
black swan

ngaya — *nigh a*
I am

Nura — *noo ra*
Country

walan — *wal an*
rain

wandanguli — *wan dang gooli*
wattle

warada — *wara da*
waratah

warami — *wara me*
hello

wirriga — *wirr iga*
goanna

wiyanga — *wi yan ga*
mother

wubin — *wob in*
feather-tailed glider

wumbat — *wum bat*
wombat

yabun — *ye bun*
music made by clapping sticks

yana — *ya na*
walk

yanada — *yana da*
moon

yanu — *ya nu*
goodbye

yellamundie — *yella mundie*
storyteller

yibban-da — *yibb an da*
singing

yiluk — *yil uk*
sun

yuruka — *yur uka*
hot

About Darug Country

COOEE MITTIGAR.
Come here friend.

Welcome to our Daruga Nura story.
For thousands of years we Darug people have cared for Country and Country has cared for us.

Our people have lived in the greater Sydney basin for thousands of years. Darug Country stretches far — reaching our Kuringgai neighbours in the north east, our Darkinjung neighbours to the north, our Wiradjuri neighbours to the west and our Gandangara neighbours in the south.

For millennia our people were many. Darug Nura was fertile. It gave us plentiful supplies of fruits, vegetables, grains, fish and meat. Our Elders passed down all the knowledge we needed to prepare vegetables and fruit, to hunt and fish, and to heal our injuries or illnesses with medicinal plants that were readily available.

Our Country was where the First Fleet came ashore in 1788. It was the Darug people's Homelands that were the first colonised, and as a result, our Darug people suffered greatly. By early 1789 smallpox had spread rapidly among our people, killing at least half of our ancestors within three months.

The Sydney Basin saw long and ongoing frontier wars and our Darug people fought hard to protect and preserve Country and culture.

Protection of Country – of culture – of stories and language is important to us as the original custodians of Darug Nura. But it is not only important for us, the Darug – it is important for everyone. Sharing what our people have known for thousands of years about caring for Country; learning medicine and Law passed down over hundreds of generations through our Elders; keeping our stories alive and our language on our tongues; all of these things are gifts to everyone who visits and walks with us.

Warami mittigar. Hello friend.

Welcome to Daruga Nura.

About the author

JASMINE SEYMOUR is a Darug woman belonging to the Boorooberongal people of the Dyirabun–Hawkesbury region of New South Wales. She is a descendant of the Aboriginal community that was devastated by colonists soon after their arrival in 1788.

Jasmine is the fifth generation great-granddaugther of Maria Lock, daughter of Boorooberongal chief, Yarramundi. She is a primary school teacher, writer, artist and mother of two boys.

Jasmine is a member of the Darug Custodian Aboriginal Corporation and secretary of the Da Murrytoola — the Hawkesbury region branch of the Aboriginal Education Consultation Group.

Jasmine is also the author illustrator of *Baby Business*, published by Magabala Books.

About the artist

LEANNE MULGO WATSON is a Darug woman from the Boorooberongal people of the Dyirabun–Hawkesbury region of New South Wales. She is a mother and a grandmother.

Leanne works on Country with community, in many professional roles, learning from Elders how to improve and care for community culture, cultural sites, landforms and the environment.

Leanne has been a Director of the Darug Custodian Aboriginal Corporation for many years.

As an artist-educator, Leanne works with a wide range of education facilities, museums and cultural groups, and her work on the Darug seasonal calendar has, in collaboration with Jasmine Seymour, evolved into this book. Leanne believes that education is the key to culture staying strong.

For Leanne and Jasmine it is very important to share Darug language and culture and show that the Darug people are still strong on Country. They hope that *Cooee Mittigar* will contribute to the continuation of stories and culture.

To our Darug Elders past, present and future,
and for all the children on Darug Nura
J S & L M W

Special thanks
Didgerigore
to our Darug djuramin.
And to Linda Bellamy
for her supportive feedback.

First published 2019, reprinted 2020
Magabala Books Aboriginal Corporation,
Broome, Western Australia
Website: www.magabala.com
Email: sales@magabala.com

Magabala Books receives financial assistance from
the Commonwealth Government through the Australia Council,
its arts advisory body. The State of Western Australia has made an
investment in this project through the Department of Local Government,
Sport and Cultural Industries. Magabala Books would like to acknowledge
the generous support of the Shire of Broome, Western Australia.

978-1-925936-86-5

All languages, whether passed down in spoken or
written form, change from one generation to the
next as speakers revitalise their mother tongues.
The Darug language we use in *Cooee Mittigar*
has been carefully considered.
Some Darug people may use alternative names
for animals, plants or Country to those we have
used in this book.

A catalogue record for this
book is available from the
National Library of Australia

NATIONAL
LIBRARY
OF AUSTRALIA

The illustrations for this book are digital collage. They feature mixed media
images comprising acrylic painting, mono-prints and stencil printing.

Packaged by Ballantyne Rawlins in collaboration with Magabala Books
Printed in China by Toppan Leefung Printing Ltd.

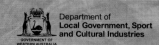

Australian Government

Australia Council for the Arts

Department of
Local Government, Sport
and Cultural Industries
GOVERNMENT OF
WESTERN AUSTRALIA

Shire of
Broome
people · place · prosperity